DAD I WROTE THIS BOOK ABOUT YOU

What I Love About You Dad!

ISBN-13: 978-1-952663-15-4

“

I love how we all know I am your favorite child Dad!

to: ____________________

from: ________________

My father gave me the greatest gift anyone could give another person, he believed in me.

- Jim Valvano

Dad & Me

My Dad is

You Love to

You Taught Me How To

Favorite thing about my Dad is

"
No man stands taller than when he stoops to help a child.
- Abraham Lincoln

You are Most Happy When

You are Funny When

You are Good at

Our favorite thing to do together is

I Can't Forget the Day You

My father didn't tell me how to live. He lived, and let me watch him do it.

- Clarence Budington Kelland

You are Super Awesome Because

You Carry Me When

You Help Me To

You Make Me Laugh By

You Find Time To

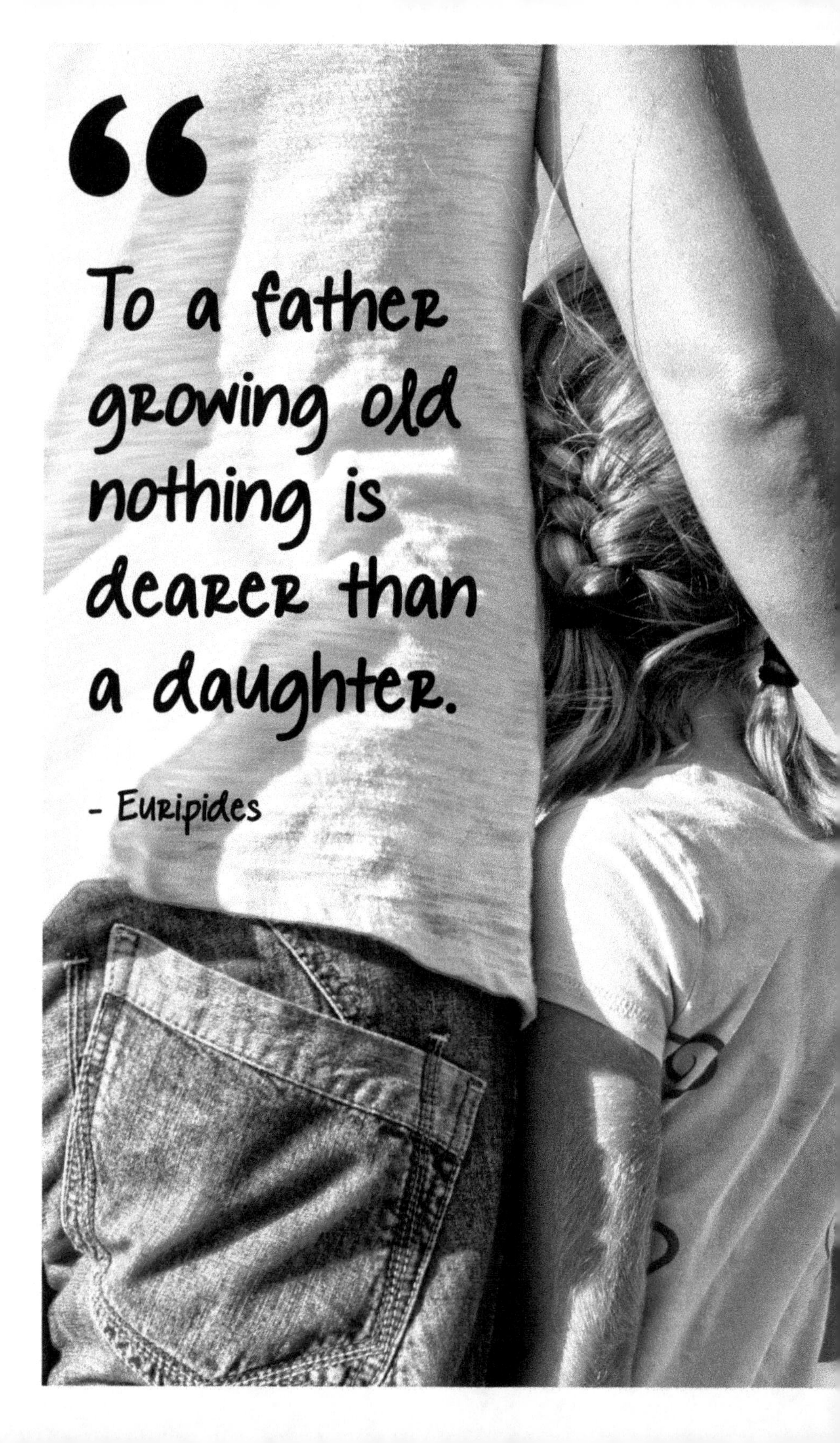
"
To a father growing old nothing is dearer than a daughter.
- Euripides

You Work Hard At

You Make My Favorite Food of

You Take Care of Me By

He Gives The Best

You are The Happiest When

Anyone can be a father,
but it takes someone special
to be a dad, and that's why
I call you dad, because
you are so special to me.
You taught me the game
and you taught me
how to play it right.

– Wade Boggs

You Made Me Believe I

I Love The Way You

You Listen To Me When

You Gave Me Rides To

You Said I Could

Daddies don't just love their children every now and then, it's a love without end.

- George Strait

You Sang To Me while

You Let Me Ride On

I love The Way You Play

I Love The Way You Love

You Let Me Have

My dad's my best mate, and he always will be.

- Cher Lloyd

You are Always There When

You are Strong When You

You Supported Me When

You Encouraged Me to

You Built Me

“

You don't have to deserve your mother's love. You have to deserve your father's.

- Rober Frost

Your Willingness To

You Call Me by

I Love it When We

The Funniest Thing You Do is

You Love it When I

It is admirable for a man to take his son fishing, but there is a special place in heaven for the father who takes his daughter shopping.

- John Sinor

You are Such a Good

The Best
Thing About
You is

Our Shared Love of

How you Used to Bring Me

You Found a Way To

“

To her, the name of father was another name for love.

- Fanny Fern

You Always Watch

You Know Just The Right

You are My Hero Because

My Best Memories of You are

“

He adopted a role called being a father so that his child would have something mythical and infinitely important: a protector.

- Tom Wolfe

Dad & Me

Note

Appreciation

We Congratulate you on your journey so Far. Thank you For Buying our Little Book of Love.
If you Enjoyed This Book, Take a little of your Time To Rate Us on Amazon.

We'll Very Much Appreciate it.

C.J

Other Book By The Same Author

CPSIA information can be obtained
at www.ICGtesting.com
Printed in the USA
BVHW021545220621
610213BV00005B/746